A Day on the Prairie

By: Third Grade Students

Kildeer Countryside School

We dedicate our story
to a book that helped us
get our minds churning
with amazing words...

THE THESAURUS!

MEET THE AUTHORS

BACK ROW
Maddie Wilhem, Aidan O'Connell, Grayson Mick, Sarah Pentek, Caroline Hartwell, Dylan Irlbeck, Jahnavi Kishore, Abbigal Speck

FRONT ROW
Ilana Kopelman, Melanie Blake, Hannah Petrich, Madison Randol, Aki Dhadda, Morghan Murphy, Alaina Errico, Mazzy Teich

The prairie sun rises from the east.

Robins fly through the clear sky, singing along with the wind.

White-tailed deer prance through the thick, tall grass.

Turtles wake up in the crisp fall air, and I begin a walk
through the dewy grass.

I smell the fresh water of a crystal blue painted stream
sparkling in the shimmering sunrise.

I smell the nectar of the purple petals from the pretty prairie clover.

I see a red-tailed hawk swooping through the cool, breezy air as he chases a tiny field mouse scurrying to safety.

I see a hurried black-tailed prairie dog
digging its burrow deep under the lush prairie soil.

I feel a radiant orange and black Monarch butterfly's wing flapping by my face as it gently lands on my shoulder.

I feel the smooth softness of a downy killdeer feather caught while it slowly floated to the prairie floor.

I touch soft, cottonlike milkweed
dancing with the breeze.

I touch the elegant jeweled shooting star peeking out of
a pile of decaying leaves.

I taste the ghastly smoke and ashes from the distant prairie fires.

I taste tangy, juicy blueberries fresh from the plump bush.

I hear the carrion beetle chirping under the painted blue sky.

I hear a pack of wolves howling as the Moon rises and the Sun disappears behind the tall bluestem grass.

I wonder where the whistling wind will carry the
tiny tufts of dandelion seeds.

I wonder what's rustling the bushes as I see a pair of flashy emerald eyes staring at me.

I hope people enjoy walking through the lush and beautiful prairie, leaving nothing but their footprints.

I hope the shimmering stream stays crystal clear so all prairie animals and plants can live in harmony forever.

The magical sunset gracefully sets as it starts to lightly drizzle.

The rain glitters on the birch trees and tickles a goldenrod spider's web.

The Moon rises over the prairie as it slowly falls asleep.

Mosquitoes nip at the coat of a white-tailed deer,
and then everything goes quiet.

And then...faintly I hear owls waking and starting
to rise to hunt in the night sky.

PRAIRIE PLANTS AND FLOWERS

Shortgrass, Mixed Grass, Tallgrass, Prairie Wetlands, Big Bluestem, Blue Grama Grass, Buffalo Grass, Canada Wild Rye, Indian Grass, June Grass, Little Bluestem, Porcupine Grass, Prairie Cordgrass, Prairie Dropseed, Sideoats Grama, Black-Eyed Susan, Common Spiderwort, Jewelweed, Prairie Blazing Star, Prickly Pear Cactus, Purple Coneflower, Purple Prairie Clover, Western Prairie Fringed Orchid, Wild Bergamot, Blueberry Bush, Milkweed, Jeweled Shooting Star, Dandelion

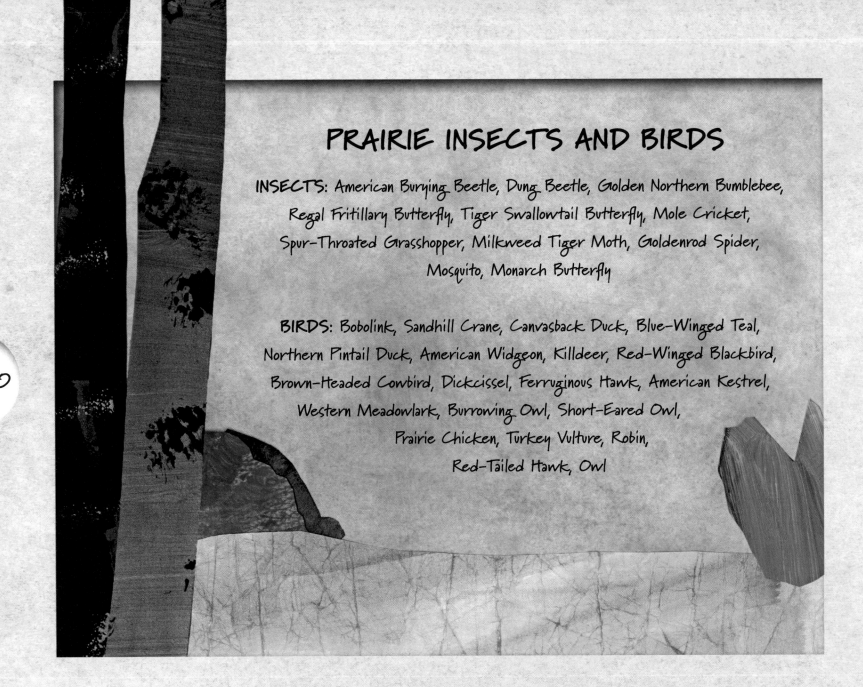

PRAIRIE INSECTS AND BIRDS

INSECTS: American Burying Beetle, Dung Beetle, Golden Northern Bumblebee, Regal Fritillary Butterfly, Tiger Swallowtail Butterfly, Mole Cricket, Spur-Throated Grasshopper, Milkweed Tiger Moth, Goldenrod Spider, Mosquito, Monarch Butterfly

BIRDS: Bobolink, Sandhill Crane, Canvasback Duck, Blue-Winged Teal, Northern Pintail Duck, American Widgeon, Killdeer, Red-Winged Blackbird, Brown-Headed Cowbird, Dickcissel, Ferruginous Hawk, American Kestrel, Western Meadowlark, Burrowing Owl, Short-Eared Owl, Prairie Chicken, Turkey Vulture, Robin, Red-Tailed Hawk, Owl

PRAIRIE ANIMALS

Pocket Gopher, Snapping Turtle, Spadefoot Toad, Tiger Salamander, Western Box Turtle, Woodchuck, Badger, Grizzly Bear, Black-Footed Ferret, Raccoon, Eastern Spotted Skunk, Bison, Mule Deer, White-Tailed Deer, Elk, Pronghorn, Eastern Cottontail, Black-Tailed Jackrabbit, Harvest Mouse, Black-Tailed Prairie Dog, Coyote, Gray Fox, Swift Fox, Gray Wolf, Brazilian Free-Tailed Bat, Hognose Snake, Massasauga Rattlesnake

Kids Are Authors®
Books written by children for children

The Kids Are Authors® Competition was established in 1986 to encourage children to read and to become involved
in the creative process of writing.

Since then, thousands of children have written and illustrated books as participants in the Kids Are Authors® Competition.

The winning books in the annual competition are published by Scholastic Inc.
and are distributed by Scholastic Book Fairs throughout the United States.

For more information:
Kids Are Authors® 1080 Greenwood Blvd.; Lake Mary, FL 32746
Or visit our web site at: www.scholastic.com/kidsareauthors

For information regarding permission, write to Scholastic Inc.,
Attention: Permission Department, 557 Broadway; New York, NY 10012.

Copyright © 2008 by Scholastic Inc.

Scholastic and associated logos are trademarks and/or
registered trademarks of Scholastic Inc.

ISBN 10: 0-545-11965-0

ISBN 13: 978-0-545-11965-8

12 11 10 9 8 7 6 5 4 3 2 1

Cover and Book Design by Bill Henderson

Printed and bound in the U.S.A.   First Printing, July 2008